Top Year 2 Times Tables Tests from CGP!

Times Tables are tricky, that's for sure. The best way to get to grips with them is regular doses of practice throughout the year.

That's where this CGP book comes in. It's packed with pupil-friendly 10-Minute Workouts — one for every week of Year 2. Each one covers a mixture of Times Tables to really test their skills.

We've included all the answers in a cut-out section, and there's even a progress chart to help keep track of pupils' scores. Smashing!

Published by CGP

ISBN: 978 1 78294 866 7

Editors: Katherine Faudemer, Zoe Fenwick, Cathy Lear and Katya Parkes

Contributors: Amanda MacNaughton and Susan Foord

Reviewer: Alison Griffin

With thanks to Karen Wells for the proofreading.

With thanks to Jan Greenway for the copyright research.

Clipart from Corel®

With thanks to iStockphoto.com for permission to reproduce the photographs used on pages 59 and 82.

Contains public sector information licensed under the Open Government Licence v3.0 http://www.nationalarchives.gov.uk/doc/open-government-licence/version/3/

Printed by Elanders Ltd, Newcastle upon Tyne.

Based on the classic CGP style created by Richard Parsons.

Text, design, layout and original illustrations © Coordination Group Publications Ltd. (CGP) 2017 All rights reserved.

How to Use this Book

- This book contains <u>36 workouts</u>. We've split them into <u>3 sections</u> — one for each term, with <u>12 workouts</u> each. There's roughly one workout for <u>every week</u> of the school year.

- Each workout is out of <u>12 marks</u> and should take about <u>10 minutes</u>.

- Each workout starts with some '<u>get started</u>' <u>questions</u>, before moving on to some <u>worded questions</u> and <u>problems</u>.

- Each workout ends with a fun <u>puzzle</u> to challenge pupils who finish the other questions. Some puzzles draw in other maths that pupils will have already covered.

- <u>Pictorial questions</u> are used when a times table is first introduced. The workouts then <u>increase in difficulty</u> as you go through the book.

- <u>Answers</u> and a <u>Progress Chart</u> can be found at the <u>back</u> of the book.

The <u>contents pages</u> show where each times table is tested, and any <u>extra maths</u> tested in the <u>puzzles</u>.

Each <u>new times table</u> is introduced on its own. As pupils become more familiar with the times tables, <u>two</u> or <u>three</u> times tables are covered together.

This means the workouts in each term can be done in an order which <u>best suits</u> the <u>needs</u> of your class.

The <u>tick boxes</u> on the contents pages can help you to keep a <u>record</u> of which workouts have been attempted.

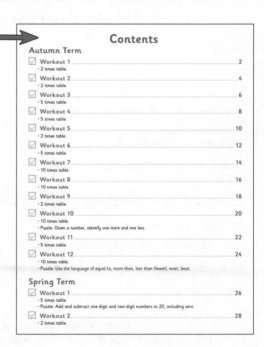

Contents

Summer Term

Get Started

Fill in the missing numbers. Use the pictures to help you.

1. a) 2 × 2 = ...

    _____
    1 mark

   b) 3 × 2 = ...

    _____
    1 mark

   c) 4 × 2 = ...

    _____
    1 mark

   d) 5 × 2 = ...

    _____
    1 mark

Now try these:

2. Write the number of pairs of elephants in the picture, then write the total number of elephants in the picture.

   .... pairs

            .... elephants

    _____
    2 marks

2

3. Answer these multiplications.

a) $6 \times 2 = $ ....

d) $9 \times 2 = $ ....

b) $12 \times 2 = $ ....

e) $7 \times 2 = $ ....

c) $11 \times 2 = $ ....

f) $5 \times 2 = $ ....

6 marks

How did you do?

Score:

Puzzle: Farah the Fish

Farah the fish has got lost! Help her find her way home.
She must follow the two times table in order.
Start at the bubble which is the same as 1×2,
then find 2×2, then 3×2 until you get to 12×2.

Join the bubbles to show Farah the way home.

Puzzle Complete?

Get Started

Fill in the missing numbers. Use the pictures to help you.

1. a) 4 × 2 = ...

1 mark

   b) 5 × 2 = ...

1 mark

   c) 6 × 2 = ...

1 mark

   d) 7 × 2 = ...

1 mark

Now try these:

2. Write the number of pairs of shoes in the picture, then write the total number of shoes in the picture.

      .... pairs

      .... shoes

2 marks

4

3. Answer these multiplications.

a) 9 × 2 = ...

b) 8 × 2 = ...

c) 12 × 2 = ...

d) 3 × 2 = ...

e) 7 × 2 = ...

f) 10 × 2 = ...

6 marks

How did you do?

Score:

Puzzle: Where is Rufus?

Rufus has left a note to tell his friends where he is.
His note is in code. Work out the answers to the calculations.
Then use the table to work out the code.

6 × 2 =   2 × 2 =   1 × 2 =   3 × 2 =   4 × 2 =

....

8 × 2 =   5 × 2 =   7 × 2 =   9 × 2 =

....

2	4	6	8	10	12	14	16	18
T	N	H	E	A	I	R	P	K

Where is Rufus? ....

....

Puzzle Complete?

Get Started

Fill in the missing numbers. Use the pictures to help you.

1. a) 2 × 5 = ...

    1 mark

    b) 3 × 5 = ...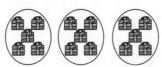

    1 mark

    c) 4 × 5 = ...

    1 mark

    d) 5 × 5 = ...

    1 mark

Now try these:

2. Write the number of groups of balloons in the picture,
    then write the total number of balloons in the picture.

    .... groups

    .... balloons

    2 marks

6

3. Answer these multiplications.

a) 10 × 5 = ...

b) 12 × 5 = ...

c) 11 × 5 = ...

d) 8 × 5 = ...

e) 6 × 5 = ...

f) 9 × 5 = ...

6 marks

How did you do?

Score:

Puzzle: Molly's Bananas

Molly has lost all of her bananas. Bananas that belong to
Molly have a number from the 5 times table written on them.
Draw a circle around each of the bananas that belong to Molly.

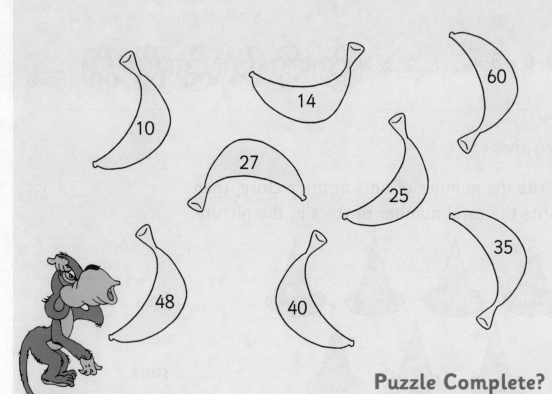

Puzzle Complete?

Get Started

Fill in the missing numbers. Use the pictures to help you.

1. a) 3 × 5 = ...

   1 mark

   b) 4 × 5 = ...

   1 mark

   c) 5 × 5 = ...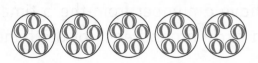

   1 mark

   d) 6 × 5 = ...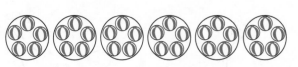

   1 mark

Now try these:

2. Write the number of hats in the picture, then write the total number of stars in the picture.

.... hats

.... stars

2 marks

3. Answer these multiplications.

    a) 11 × 5 = ...   d) 7 × 5 = ...

    b) 2 × 5 = ...   e) 8 × 5 = ...

    c) 10 × 5 = ...   f) 12 × 5 = ...

                                                        ‾‾‾‾‾‾
                                                        6 marks

How did you do?   Score:

Puzzle: Colour the Rocket

Colour in the parts of the rocket which are
labelled with numbers from the five times table.

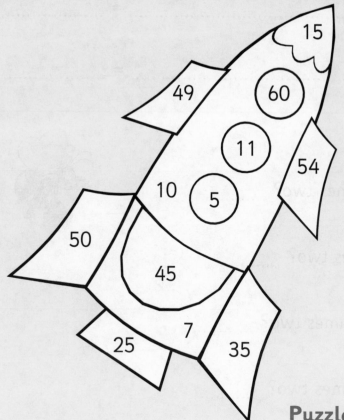

Puzzle Complete?

Get Started

1. You can write multiplications as additions.
   Fill in the missing numbers from the 2 times table.

   a) 2 × 2 = 2 + 2 = ...

   b) 3 × 2 = ... + ...+ .... = ...

   c) 4 × 2 = ... = ...

   d) 5 × 2 = ... = ...

   e) 6 × 2 = ... = ...

   5 marks

Now try these:

2. What is eight times two? ....

   1 mark

3. What is ten times two? ....

   1 mark

4. What is twelve times two? ....

   1 mark

5. What is seven times two? ....

   1 mark

10

6. What is six times two? ....

1 mark

7. What is four times two? ....

1 mark

8. What is nine times two? ....

1 mark

How did you do?

Score:

Puzzle: Basketball Competition

Sara, Lily and Ash are playing basketball.
They get 2 points for each goal they score.
Work out how many points they each scored.

Sara   Lily   Ash

4 goals   6 goals   9 goals

= .... points   = ... points   = ... points

Usman is also playing. He scores 20 points.
How many goals did he score?

.... goals

Puzzle Complete?

Autumn Term: Workout 5

Get Started

1. You can write multiplications as additions.
    Fill in the missing numbers from the 5 times table.

    a) 2 × 5 = 5 + 5 = ...

    b) 3 × 5 = ... + ... + ... = ...

    c) 4 × 5 = ... = ...

    d) 5 × 5 = ... = ...

    e) 6 × 5 = ... = ...

    5 marks

Now try these:

2. What is eleven times five? ....

    1 mark

3. What is nine times five? ....

    1 mark

4. What is seven times five? ....

    1 mark

5. What is ten times five? ....

    1 mark

6. What is twelve times five? …………

1 mark

7. What is eight times five? …………

1 mark

8. What is three times five? …………

1 mark

How did you do?

Score:

Puzzle: Kangaroo Jump

Some kangaroos are jumping along a number line.
The calculations show how far each kangaroo will jump.
Draw a ring around the answer on the number line.

11 × 5

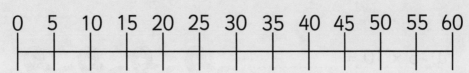

0 5 10 15 20 25 30 35 40 45 50 55 60

5 × 5

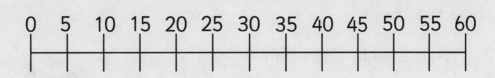

0 5 10 15 20 25 30 35 40 45 50 55 60

8 × 5

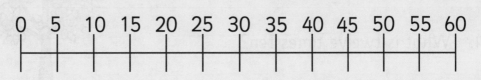

0 5 10 15 20 25 30 35 40 45 50 55 60

Puzzle Complete?

---

(10)

Fill in the missing numbers.   Use the pictures to help you.

1. a) 2 × 10 = ...

1 mark

    b) 3 × 10 = ...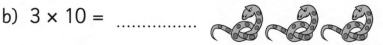

1 mark

    c) 4 × 10 = ...

1 mark

    d) 5 × 10 = ...

1 mark

Now try these:

2. What is eight times ten? ....

1 mark

3. What is six times ten? ....

1 mark

4. What is twelve times ten? ....

1 mark

5. What is nine times ten? ....

1 mark

14

6. What is eleven times ten? ....

7. What is seven times ten? ....

8. What is ten times ten? ....

9. What is one times ten? ....

How did you do?   Score: [   ]

Puzzle: Ski Run

Norman is skiing. The ski run is marked out by trees.
He can only ski past trees with numbers from the ten times table.
Colour in all the trees that are on the ski run.

Puzzle Complete? ✓

15

10

Get Started

1. You can write multiplications as additions.
   Fill in the missing numbers from the 10 times table.

   a) $2 \times 10 = 10 + 10 =$ ....

   b) $3 \times 10 =$ .... + ... + ... = ...

   c) $5 \times 10 =$ .... = ...

   d) $7 \times 10 =$ .... = ...

   e) $8 \times 10 =$ .... = ...

   5 marks

Now try these:

2. What is twelve times ten? ....

   1 mark

3. What is seven times ten? ....

   1 mark

4. What is ten times ten? ....

   1 mark

5. What is eight times ten? ....

   1 mark

16

6. What is nine times ten? ....

7. What is one times ten? ....

8. What is eleven times ten? ....

How did you do?　　　　　　　　　　　Score:

Puzzle: Luggage Muddle

Anna and Sam's luggage has been mixed up.
Each bag has a multiplication question on it.

If the answer is **more than 60**, the bag belongs to **Anna**.

If the answer is **less than 60**, the bag belongs to **Sam**.

Draw a line to match each bag to either Anna or Sam.

1 × 10　　4 × 10　　9 × 10　　11 × 10　　7 × 10　　3 × 10

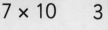

Sam

Anna

Puzzle Complete?

(10)

Get Started

1. a) 6 × 2 = ...   b) 9 × 2 = ...

_____
2 marks

2. a) 4 × 2 = ...   b) 12 × 2 = ...

_____
2 marks

3. a) 7 × 2 = ...   b) 2 × 2 = ...

_____
2 marks

Now try these:

4. What is five times two? ....

_____
1 mark

5. What is ten times two? ....

_____
1 mark

6. What is three times two? ....

_____
1 mark

18

7. Dividing is the opposite of multiplying.
   Your two times tables can help you answer these divisions.

   a) 16 ÷ 2:   8 × 2 = 16   so 16 ÷ 2 = ...

   b) 22 ÷ 2:   .... × 2 = 22   so 22 ÷ 2 = ...

   c) 8 ÷ 2:   .... so 8 ÷ 2 = ...

3 marks

How did you do?

Score:

Puzzle: Strawberry Picking

Anwar and his friends went strawberry picking.
The calculation shows how many strawberries they each picked.
Circle the basket with the most strawberries inside.

Anwar
11 × 2

= ....

Saf
7 × 2

= ....

Callie
12 × 2

= ....

Ned
9 × 2

= ....

Puzzle Complete?

Get Started

1. a) 3 × 10 = ...   b) 8 × 10 = ...

    2 marks

2. a) 10 × 10 = ...   b) 5 × 10 = ...

    2 marks

3. a) 2 × 10 = ...   b) 11 × 10 = ...

    2 marks

Now try these:

4. What is seven times ten? ....

    1 mark

5. What is nine times ten? ....

    1 mark

6. What is one times ten? ....

    1 mark

7. Dividing is the opposite of multiplying.
    Your ten times tables can help you answer these divisions.

    a) 120 ÷ 10: 12 × 10 = 120   so 120 ÷ 10 = ...

    b) 40 ÷ 10: .... × 10 = 40 so 40 ÷ 10 = ...

    c) 20 ÷ 10: .... so 20 ÷ 10 = ...

    3 marks

How did you do?   Score: [   ]

Puzzle: **Quiz Scores**

Three teams are taking part in a quiz.

- They get an extra point if they answer the star question.

- They lose a point if they cheat!

Use the table to work out their scores.

Team	Score	Star Question?	Cheated?	Total Score
Quiz Masters	2 × 10	✓		....
Quiz Heroes	5 × 10		✓	....
Quiz Kids	4 × 10	✓	✓	....

Puzzle Complete? ✓

(10)

Get Started

1. a) 7 × 5 = ...

    b) 2 × 5 = ...

    2 marks

2. a) 11 × 5 = ...

    b) 8 × 5 = ...

    2 marks

3. a) 4 × 5 = ...

    b) 1 × 5 = ...

    2 marks

Now try these:

4. What is three times five? ....

    1 mark

5. What is six times five? ....

    1 mark

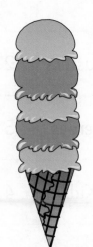

6. What is ten times five? ....

    1 mark

22

7. What is forty-five divided by five? ....

1 mark

8. What is sixty divided by five? ....

1 mark

9. What is twenty-five divided by five? ....

1 mark

How did you do?   Score:

Puzzle: Digging for Treasure

Miquita the mole is digging for treasure. How deep does she have to dig to reach each piece of treasure?

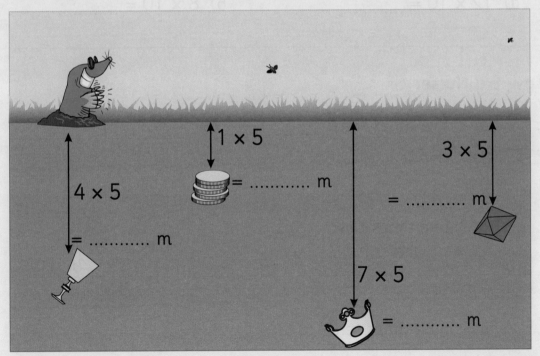

4×5

= .... m

1×5

= .... m

3×5

= .... m

7×5

= .... m

Puzzle Complete?

Get Started

1. a) 10 × 10 = ...

    b) 4 × 10 = ...

    2 marks

2. a) 7 × 10 = ...

    b) 11 × 10 = ...

    2 marks

3. a) 12 × 10 = ...

    b) 8 × 10 = ...

    2 marks

Now try these:

4. What is five times ten? ....

    1 mark

5. What is one times ten? ....

    1 mark

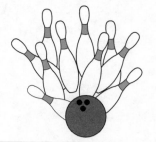

6. What is nine times ten? ....

    1 mark

24

7. What is thirty divided by ten? …………

8. What is twenty divided by ten? …………

9. What is sixty divided by ten? …………

How did you do?

Score:

Puzzle: Pancake Challenge!

Some chefs are comparing how many pancakes they have made.

Carlo	Steffi	Ben	Dana
$100 \div 10$	5×10	3×10	1×10
= …………	= …………	= …………	= …………

Fill in the gaps using less than, more than or equal to.

Steffi's number of pancakes is …………………………… Ben's.

Carlo's number of pancakes is …………………………… Dana's.

Dana's number of pancakes is …………………………… Steffi's.

Puzzle Complete?

Autumn Term: Workout 12

Spring Term: Workout 1

Get Started

1. a) $3 \times 5 =$ ....

    b) $5 \times 5 =$ ....

    2 marks

2. a) $6 \times 5 =$ ....

    b) $20 \div 5 =$ ....

    2 marks

3. a) $50 \div 5 =$ ....

    b) $8 \times 5 =$ ....

    2 marks

Now try these:

4. a) What is two times five? ....

    b) What is seven times five? ....

    c) What is eleven times five? ....

    3 marks

5. a) What is one times five? ....

    b) What is nine times five? ....

    c) What is twelve times five? ....

How did you do?   Score: [ ]

Puzzle: It's Magic!

Aleks the magician needs to work out some numbers for a magic spell.

The answers to the two clues below must add up to 20.

Complete the clues to find the magic numbers.

Clue 1

$1 \times 5 =$

....

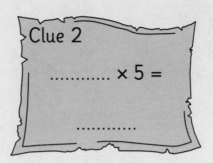

Clue 2

.... $\times 5 =$

....

Puzzle Complete?

Get Started

1. a) $9 \times 2 =$ ....

    b) $5 \times 2 =$ ....

    ___
    2 marks

2. a) $3 \times 2 =$ ....

    b) $24 \div 2 =$ ....

    ___
    2 marks

3. a) $8 \div 2 =$ ....

    b) $20 \div 2 =$ ....

    ___
    2 marks

Now try these:

4. Write how many pairs of gloves there are in the picture, then write how many gloves there are.

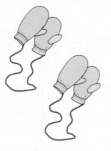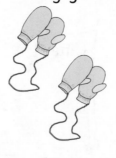

    .... pairs

    .... gloves

    ___
    2 marks

5. What is four divided by two? ....

    ___
    1 mark

28

6. a) What is eleven times two? ....

b) What is seven times two? ....

c) What is sixteen divided by two? ....

3 marks

How did you do?

Score:

Puzzle: Circus Seals

Three seals can't remember which ball is theirs!
Draw lines to match the calculations in the balls to the
correct answer on the seals.

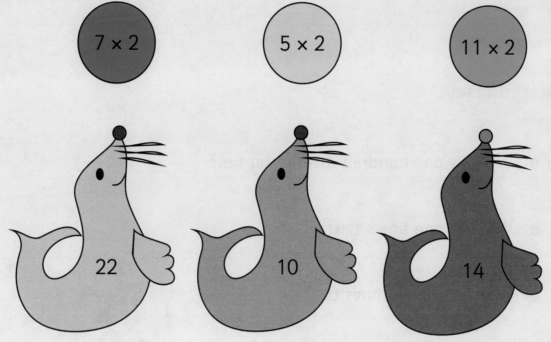

Puzzle Complete?

Spring Term: Workout 2

Get Started

1. a) 4 × 10 = ...   b) 50 ÷ 10 = ...

    2 marks

2. b) 60 ÷ 10 = ...   b) 3 × 10 = ...

    2 marks

3. a) 20 ÷ 10 = ...   b) 8 × 10 = ...

    2 marks

Now try these:

4. a) What is one hundred divided by ten? ....

    b) What is one times ten? ....

    c) What is eleven times ten? ....

    3 marks

30

5. a) What is seventy divided by ten? ....

   b) What is twelve times ten? ....

   c) What is ninety divided by ten? ....

3 marks

How did you do?

Score: [   ]

Puzzle: Maths Maze

Find a route through the maze.
You can only pass through numbers
from the 10 times table.

Start

| 60 | | 90 |

| 50 | 31 | 19 | 80 |

| 10 | 30 |

| | 70 |

| 20 | 100 |

| 80 | 26 | 40 |

| 25 | 70 | 99 | 110 | Finish

Puzzle Complete?

Get Started

1. a) 3 × 2 = ...

    b) 18 ÷ 2 = ...

    2 marks

2. a) 10 ÷ 2 = ...

    b) 11 × 10 = ...

    2 marks

3. a) 6 × 10 = ...

    b) 80 ÷ 10 = ...

    2 marks

Now try these:

4. a) What is forty divided by ten? ....

    b) What is two times ten? ....

    c) What is thirty divided by ten? ....

    3 marks

5. a) What is twelve times two? ....

    b) What is fourteen divided by two? ....

    c) What is one times two? ....

3 marks

How did you do?   **Score:** [   ]

Puzzle: Colour the Balloons

Work out the answers to the calculations in the balloons.
Colour the balloons with an answer **less than 20** in **yellow**.
Colour the rest of the balloons in **blue**.

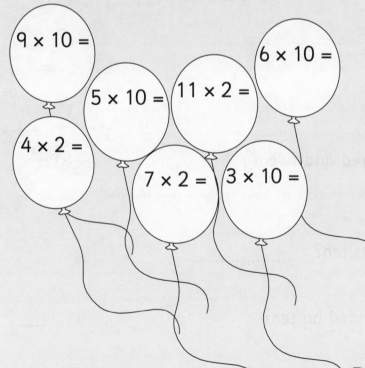

How many yellow
balloons are there?

....

How many blue
balloons are there?

....

Puzzle Complete?

Get Started

1. a) 7 × 5 = ...   b) 6 × 10 = ...

    2 marks

2. a) 2 × 10 = ...   b) 5 ÷ 5 = ...

    2 marks

3. a) 40 ÷ 5 = ...   b) 50 ÷ 10 = ...

    2 marks

Now try these:

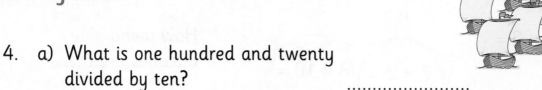

4. a) What is one hundred and twenty
    divided by ten?   ....

    b) What is three times ten? ....

    c) What is ninety divided by ten? ....

    3 marks

5. a) What is four times five? ....

   b) What is fifty divided by five? ....

   c) What is eleven times five? ....

3 marks

How did you do?

Score:

Puzzle: Help Raymond!

Raymond is trying to count backwards from 110, but he's forgotten some of the numbers. Help him by filling in the missing numbers below.

Puzzle Complete?

35

10

Get Started

1. a) $8 \times 2 = $ ....

    b) $6 \div 2 = $ ....

    2 marks

2. a) $20 \div 2 = $ ....

    b) $4 \times 5 = $ ....

    2 marks

3. a) $15 \div 5 = $ ....

    b) $9 \times 5 = $ ....

    2 marks

Now try these:

4. a) What is five times two? ....

    b) What is twenty-two divided by two? ....

    c) What is six times two? ....

    3 marks

36

5. a) What is thirty-five divided by five? ....

   b) What is eleven times five? ....

   c) What is twenty-five divided by five? ....

3 marks

How did you do?   Score: [   ]

Puzzle: Who's the Tallest?

Zara the zoo keeper is measuring her giraffes.
Work out how tall each giraffe is.
Circle the tallest one.

| Gertie: 3 × 2 m | Gordon: 5 × 1 m | Garry: 8 ÷ 2 m |
| = ... m | = ... m | = ... m |

Puzzle Complete?

Spring Term: Workout 7

Get Started

1. a) $6 \times 5 =$ ....

    b) $25 \div 5 =$ ....

    2 marks

2. a) $15 \div 5 =$ ....

    b) $8 \times 10 =$ ....

    2 marks

3. a) $7 \times 10 =$ ....

    b) $110 \div 10 =$ ....

    2 marks

Now try these:

4. a) What is twelve lots of five? ....

    b) What is forty-five divided by five? ....

    c) What is two times five? ....

    3 marks

5. a) How many tens make forty? ....

    b) What is ten times one? ....

    c) What is one hundred divided by ten? ....

    <u>3 marks</u>

How did you do?

Score: [ ]

Puzzle: Find the Mouse's Hole

Three mice have forgotten where they live.
The number on the mouse and the number of its hole add up
to 20. Work out which mouse lives in which hole.

5 × 3 =
....

80 ÷ 10 =
....

2 × 5 =
....

10 × 1 =
....

1 × 5 =
....

120 ÷ 10 =
....

Puzzle Complete?

Spring Term: Workout 7

Get Started

1. a) $5 \times 2 =$ ....
    b) $30 \div 10 =$ ....

    _____
    2 marks

2. a) $7 \times 10 =$ ....
    b) $11 \times 2 =$ ....

    _____
    2 marks

3. a) $12 \div 2 =$ ....
    b) $50 \div 10 =$ ....

    _____
    2 marks

Now try these:

4. There are 10 spots on each t-shirt.
    Write how many t-shirts and spots there are.

.... t-shirts

.... spots

_____
2 marks

5. What is eight times two? ....

    _____
    1 mark

6. a) What is twelve multiplied by ten? ....

    b) What is ten divided by ten? ....

    c) What is eight divided by two? ....

3 marks

How did you do?

Score:

Puzzle: Number Machines

The machines below turn the numbers they are given into 20.
Help check that the machines are working properly by filling in
the missing numbers for each machine.

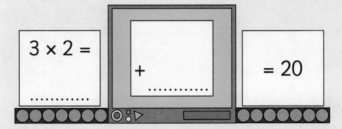

3 x 2 =

....

+

....

= 20

7 x 10 =

....

–

....

= 20

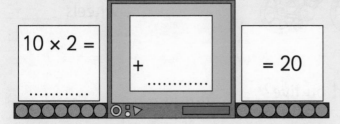

10 x 2 =

....

+

....

= 20

Puzzle Complete?

10

Get Started

1. a) $6 \times 2 =$ ....

    b) $6 \times 5 =$ ....

2. a) $55 \div 5 =$ ....

    b) $20 \div 2 =$ ....

3. a) $18 \div$ .... $= 2$

    b) .... $\times 5 = 40$

Now try these:

4. The bikes below have 2 wheels each.
    Write how many bikes and wheels there are.

.... bikes

.... wheels

5. What is thirty-five divided by five? ....

---

6. a) What is twelve lots of two? ....

    b) What is nine times five? ....

    c) What is six divided by two? ....

3 marks

How did you do?

Score: [   ]

Puzzle: Magic Potions

Meg the witch made a shrinking potion, but she drank too much!

Use a ruler to measure how tall Meg is (from her feet to the top of her hat).

How tall is Meg? .... cm

Meg casts a spell to make herself four times bigger. How tall is she now?

.... cm

Puzzle Complete?

Get Started

1. a) $7 \times 2 =$ ....   b) $5 \times 2 =$ ....

2 marks

2. a) $22 \div 2 =$ ....   b) $12 \div 2 =$ ....

2 marks

3. a) $6 \times 10 =$ ....   b) $30 \div 10 =$ ....

2 marks

Now try these:

4. a) What is eight times two? ....

    b) What is one multiplied by two? ....

2 marks

5. a) What is ninety divided by ten? ....

    b) What are twelve tens? ....

2 marks

6.   How many tens make twenty? ....

7.   Nabila counts ten ladybirds in her garden. Each ladybird has four spots. How many spots are there in total?

....

How did you do?   Score: [   ]

Puzzle: Pirate Treasure!

Captain Polly is collecting treasure from her crew.
Each pirate must give her a fraction of their treasure.

- Work out the division, then colour in the number of coins each pirate must give to Polly.

- Then circle whether they give her $\frac{1}{2}$ or $\frac{1}{4}$ of their total number of coins.

 Pirate Pete: 15 ÷ 5 = ...

$\frac{1}{2}$ or $\frac{1}{4}$

 Pirate Paul: 50 ÷ 10 = ...

$\frac{1}{2}$ or $\frac{1}{4}$

Puzzle Complete?

Get Started

1. a) $10 \times 2 =$ ....

    b) $24 \div 2 =$ ....

    2 marks

2. a) $35 \div 5 =$ ....

    b) $4 \times 5 =$ ....

    2 marks

3. a) .... $\times 5 = 45$

    b) $16 \div$ .... $= 2$

    2 marks

Now try these:

4. a) What multiplies by five to give thirty? ....

    b) What is six times two? ....

    2 marks

5. a) What is eight divided by two? ....

    b) What are eleven fives? ....

    2 marks

6. What is forty divided by five? ....

7. Becca has 2 dogs. She wants to give them 5 treats each. How many treats does she need?

....

How did you do?

Score:

Puzzle: Which Broomstick?

Kelly the Witch wants to buy the fastest broomstick. Work out the answers to the calculations to show how long it takes each broomstick to fly 500 m. Circle the fastest broomstick.

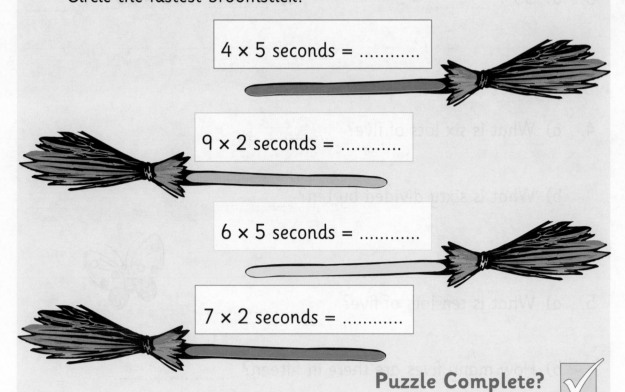

4×5 seconds = ...

9×2 seconds = ...

6×5 seconds = ...

7×2 seconds = ...

Puzzle Complete?

47

Spring Term: Workout 12

Get Started

1. a) $4 \times 5 =$ ....

    b) $45 \div 5 =$ ....

    _____
    2 marks

2. a) $80 \div 10 =$ ....

    b) $7 \times 10 =$ ....

    _____
    2 marks

3. a) $55 \div$ .... $= 5$

    b) .... $\times 10 = 20$

    _____
    2 marks

Now try these:

4. a) What is six lots of five? ....

    b) What is sixty divided by ten? ....

    _____
    2 marks

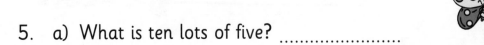

5. a) What is ten lots of five? ....

    b) How many fives are there in fifteen? ....

    _____
    2 marks

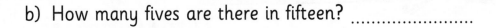

6. What is twelve lots of five? ....

7. Rayan has 9 bags of sweets. There are 10 sweets
    in each bag. How many sweets are there in total?

....

How did you do?   Score:

Puzzle: Balance the Scales

Bernie wants to balance his scales so that the calculations
on the left and the right have the same answer.
Help him find the missing numbers.

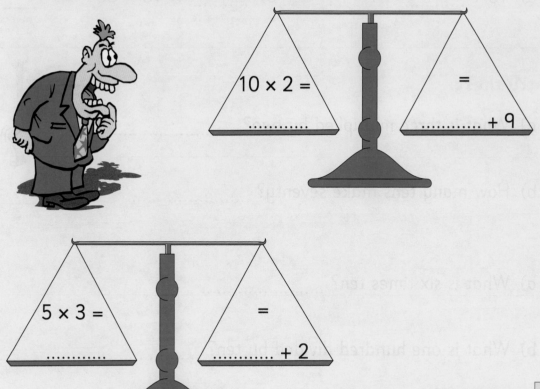

10 × 2 =   =
.... + 9

5 × 3 =   =
.... + 2

Puzzle Complete?

Get Started

1. a) 7 × 2 = ...   b) 5 × 2 = ...

    _____
    2 marks

2. a) 40 ÷ 10 = ...   b) 22 ÷ 2 = ...

    _____
    2 marks

3. a) 18 ÷ .... = 9   b) .... × 10 = 80

    _____
    2 marks

Now try these:

4. a) What is three multiplied by two? ....

    b) How many tens make seventy? ....

    _____
    2 marks

5. a) What is six times ten? ....

    b) What is one hundred divided by ten? ....

    _____
    2 marks

6. What is twelve lots of ten? ....

7. A toy car has 4 wheels. Sadia has 2 toy cars.
How many wheels are there in total?

....

1 mark

How did you do?   Score: [　　]

Puzzle: Moon Maths

Planet Uggle has 4 moons.
Beeza has **twice** as many moons as Uggle.
Oog has **10 times** as many moons as Beeza.
Rog has **10 times** as many moons as Uggle.

Write the number of moons that each planet has.

Then write a < , > or = sign in each box to compare the
number of moons.

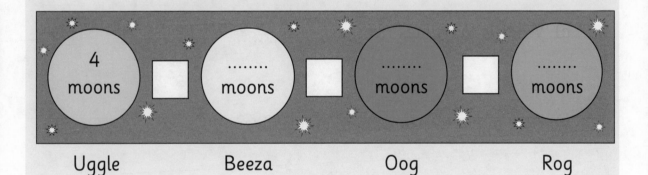

Uggle   Beeza   Oog   Rog

Puzzle Complete?

Summer Term: Workout 2

Get Started

1. a) $4 \times 5 =$ .... b) $70 \div 10 =$ ....

    ___
    2 marks

2. a) $35 \div 5 =$ .... b) $6 \times 10 =$ ....

    ___
    2 marks

3. a) $10 \div$ .... $= 2$ b) .... $\times 5 = 45$

    ___
    2 marks

Now try these:

4. a) How many twos make twenty? ....

    b) What is five times five? ....

    ___
    2 marks

5. a) How many fives are there in fifty-five? ....

    b) What is four multiplied by ten? ....

    ___
    2 marks

6. How many tens make one hundred? ....

7. Tess has 3 pizzas. She cuts each pizza into 5 slices.
    How many slices of pizza does she have in total?

    ....

How did you do?   Score:

Puzzle: Jumping Around

Each animal below always jumps the same distance.
The total each animal jumps is shown on the right.
How far have they moved altogether after each jump?

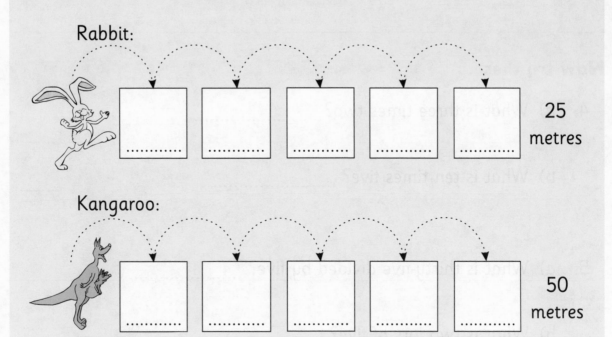

Rabbit:

| | | | | | 25 metres |

Kangaroo:

| | | | | | 50 metres |

Puzzle Complete?

Get Started

1. a) $9 \times 2 =$ ....

   b) $4 \times 2 =$ ....

   2 marks

2. a) $8 \times 5 =$ ....

   b) $22 \div 2 =$ ....

   2 marks

3. a) .... $\div 2 = 7$

   b) .... $\times 5 = 55$

   2 marks

Now try these:

4. a) What is three times two? ....

   b) What is ten times five? ....

   2 marks

5. a) What is thirty-five divided by five? ....

   b) What is two lots of five? ....

   2 marks

6. What is ten divided by two? ....

7. Kyle counts 6 ducks on the pond. Each duck has
    5 ducklings. How many ducklings are there?

    ....

How did you do?

Score:

Puzzle: Crossing the River

Explorer India Bones is crossing a bridge over a river.
There is a calculation on each plank of the bridge.

* If the answer is an **even number**, the plank is **safe**.

* If the answer is an **odd number**, the plank will **fall into the river**.

Colour the safe planks to show how to cross the river.

Puzzle Complete?

Get Started

1. a) $9 \times 2 =$ ....   b) $7 \times 5 =$ ....

    2 marks

2. a) $3 \times 5 =$ ....   b) $40 \div 10 =$ ....

    2 marks

3. a) $6 \times 10 =$ ....   b) $11 \times 2 =$ ....

    2 marks

Now try these:

4. a) What is six multiplied by two? ....

    b) What is fifty-five divided by five? ....

    c) What is eight times ten? ....

    3 marks

56

5. a) What is sixteen divided by two? ....

    b) What is nine times five? ....

    c) What is thirty divided by ten? ....

    _____
    3 marks

How did you do?   **Score:** [   ]

Puzzle: Match the Shapes!

Write the correct name inside each shape.
Then match the correct shape to the clues below.

This shape has 2 × 2 sides.
All the sides are the same length.

....

This shape has 15 ÷ 5 sides.
All the sides are the same length.

....

This shape has 40 ÷ 10 sides.
Two of the sides are
longer than the rest.

....

Puzzle Complete?

Summer Term: Workout 4

Get Started

1. a) $1 \times 2 =$ ....   b) $4 \times 5 =$ ....

   2 marks

2. a) $10 \div 5 =$ ....   b) $10 \div 10 =$ ....

   2 marks

3. a) $5 \times 10 =$ ....   b) $8 \div 2 =$ ....

   2 marks

Now try these:

4. a) What is six lots of two? ....

   b) What is five times five? ....

   c) What is seven multiplied by ten? ....

   3 marks

5. a) What is four divided by two? ....

    b) What is thirty divided by five? ....

    c) What is ninety divided by ten? ....

3 marks

How did you do?   Score:

Puzzle: Piggy Banks

Work out the answers to the calculations.
Then match the coins to the correct piggy bank.

1 × £5 =
....

5 × £2 =
....

2 × £2 =
....

Puzzle Complete?

Summer Term: Workout 5

Get Started

1. a) 5 × 2 = ...

    b) 10 ÷ 5 = ...

    _____
    2 marks

2. a) .... × 5 = 5

    b) 10 × 10 = ...

    _____
    2 marks

3. a) 20 ÷ 10 = ...

    b) .... ÷ 2 = 7

    _____
    2 marks

Now try these:

4. a) What is ten times two? ....

    b) How many fives make forty? ....

    _____
    2 marks

5. a) What is eleven times ten? ....

    b) What is twenty-four divided by two? ....

    _____
    2 marks

6. What is ten times five? ....

7. Greg bakes 12 trays of cookies. He can fit 10 cookies on
    each tray. How many cookies does he bake in total?

....

How did you do?   Score:

Puzzle: The Longest Snake Contest

These snakes are trying to win the Longest Snake Contest.
Answer the calculations to show how long each snake is.
Circle the winning snake.
Write a < , > or = sign in each box to compare their lengths.

6×5 = ... m 4×10 = ... m 12×2 = ... m

How much longer is the longest snake than
the shortest snake?

....

Puzzle Complete?

10

Get Started

1. a) 18 ÷ 2 = ...

    b) 4 × 10 = ...

    2 marks

2. a) 11 × 5 = ...

    b) 15 ÷ 5 = ...

    2 marks

3. a) .... × 10 = 60

    b) .... ÷ 2 = 11

    2 marks

Now try these:

4. a) How many twos make twelve? ....

    b) What is thirty-five divided by five? ....

    2 marks

5. a) What is eighty divided by ten? ....

    b) What is eight times two? ....

    2 marks

6. What is three lots of ten? ....

1 mark

7. There are 12 seeds in a packet. Danny has
    5 packets of seeds. How many seeds has he got in total?

    ....

1 mark

How did you do?   Score: [   ]

Puzzle: The Corner Shop

These are the prices for sweets at the corner shop.

| Jelly frog: 10p | Lemon fizzer: 5p | Chocolate mouse: 20p |

Benny has 90p. He spends 30p on lemon fizzers.
How many lemon fizzers does he buy?

....

How much money does he have left?

....

Benny spends 20p on jelly frogs. How many does he buy?

....

How much money does he have left now?

....

Puzzle Complete? ☑

Get Started

1. a) $2 \div 2 =$ ....

    b) .... $\div 10 = 5$

    2 marks

2. a) $45 \div 5 =$ ....

    b) .... $\times 2 = 4$

    2 marks

3. a) $2 \times 5 =$ ....

    b) .... $\times 10 = 10$

    2 marks

Now try these:

4. a) How many twos make six? ....

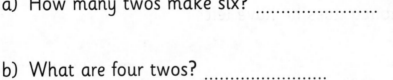

    b) What are four twos? ....

    2 marks

5. a) What is twenty divided by five? ....

    b) What is seventy divided by ten? ....

    2 marks

6. In a game, you get 10 points for landing on a red square.
    Jack lands on a red square 9 times.
    How many points does Jack have?

....

7. There are 25 red laces in a pack of sweets. Ivy shares a
    pack between 5 people. How many do they get each?

....

How did you do?

Score:

Puzzle: Space Time

The clock shows the time that Julek the
astronaut set off to fly around his planet.

He flies around the planet 9 times. It takes
him 5 minutes to fly around the planet once.

What time was it when Julek finished flying? ....

Draw the time on the clock below.

Puzzle Complete?

10

Get Started

1. a) 10 ÷ 2 = ...

    b) .... × 10 = 20

    2 marks

2. a) 6 × 5 = ...

    b) .... × 2 = 14

    2 marks

3. a) 5 ÷ 5 = ...

    b) 100 ÷ .... = 10

    2 marks

Now try these:

4. a) What is twenty divided by two? ....

    b) What is twelve lots of two? ....

    2 marks

5. a) What is one hundred and ten
        divided by ten?   ....

    b) How many fives make ten? ....

    2 marks

6. Tahir puts 12 flowers in each bunch of flowers.
    How many flowers does he need to make 10 bunches?

    ....
    _____
    1 mark

7. There are 8 muffins in a pack. Each muffin has 5 cherries
    on it. How many cherries are there in total?

    ....
    _____
    1 mark

How did you do?   **Score:**

Puzzle: Suitcase Mix-up!

Suzie is collecting her 2 suitcases at the airport, but there are
5 cases that all look the same! Use the clues to help Suzie work
out which 2 cases belong to her. Circle each of Suzie's suitcases.

Suzie's first suitcase has:

$80 \div 10$ in the tens place = ...

$4 \div 2$ in the ones place = ...

Suzie's second suitcase has:

1×5 in the tens place = ...

3×2 in the ones place = ...

Puzzle Complete?

Summer Term: Workout 9

Summer Term: Workout 10

Get Started

1. a) $24 \div 2 =$ ....

    b) $110 \div$ .... $= 11$

    2 marks

2. a) $1 \times 5 =$ ....

    b) .... $\times 2 = 4$

    2 marks

3. a) $50 \div 5 =$ ....

    b) $3 \times 10 =$ ....

    2 marks

Now try these:

4. a) What is eight divided by two? ....

    b) What is ten divided by two? ....

    2 marks

5. a) What is nine times five? ....

    b) What is six times ten? ....

    2 marks

68

6. Anila has 5 pet rabbits. She gives them 2 pieces of lettuce each. How many pieces does she give them in total?

....
<u>1 mark</u>

7. There are 11 carrots in a bag. Candice has 5 bags of carrots. How many carrots does she have in total?

....
<u>1 mark</u>

How did you do?   Score: [ ]

Puzzle: How Many Animals?

On Monday, a train carries **5 elephants** and **2 giraffes**.

On Tuesday, it has three times as many elephants and seven times as many giraffes. Fill in the number of animals below.

.... elephants   .... giraffes

How many animals is the train carrying in total on Tuesday? You can use the space below to do your working.

....

Puzzle Complete?

Get Started

1. a) $1 \times 2 =$ ....
    b) .... $\div 10 = 4$

    2 marks

2. a) $15 \div 5 =$ ....
    b) .... $\times 2 = 14$

    2 marks

3. a) $5 \times 10 =$ ....
    b) $20 \div$ .... $= 4$

    2 marks

Now try these:

4. a) How many twos make eighteen? ....

    b) What is twenty-two divided by two? ....

    2 marks

5. a) What is six times two? ....

    b) What is sixty divided by five? ....

    2 marks

6. There are 3 bees on every flower in Frankie's garden.
   There are 10 flowers. How many bees are there?

....
1 mark

7. A bowling alley has 6 lanes. Each lane has 10 pins.
   How many pins does the bowling alley have in total?

....
1 mark

How did you do?

Score:

Puzzle: Colour the Shapes

Follow the instructions below and colour in the shapes.

Circle the shapes which have $\frac{1}{2}$ of their sections shaded.

Colour
1 × 2
sections

Colour
4 ÷ 2
sections

Colour
15 ÷ 5
sections

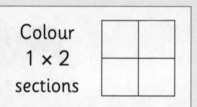

Colour
5 ÷ 5
sections

Colour
10 ÷ 5
sections

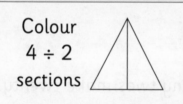

Puzzle Complete?

10

Get Started

1. a) 16 ÷ 2 = ...

    b) 20 ÷ .... = 10

    2 marks

2. a) 5 × 5 = ...

    b) 9 × .... = 18

    2 marks

3. a) 6 × 5 = ...

    b) 70 ÷ .... = 7

    2 marks

Now try these:

4. a) How many twos make twenty? ....

    b) What is seven times five? ....

    2 marks

5. a) What is eighty divided by ten? ....

    b) What is eleven lots of two? ....

    2 marks

6. 5 frogs in a pond eat 40 flies.
   They eat the same number of flies each.
   How many flies does each frog eat?

....
1 mark

7. Ewan buys 9 packs of pens. There are 10 pens in a pack.
   How many pens does he have in total?

....
1 mark

How did you do?   Score: [   ]

Puzzle: At the Sweet Shop

Work out how many of each sweet are left in the shop.
Then complete the tally chart.

8 packs of Curly Chews.
Each pack has 2 Curly Chews.

2 bags of
lollipops.
Each bag has
10 lollipops.

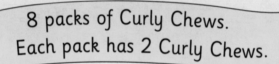

3 packs of Lemon Sours.
Each pack has
5 Lemon Sours.

Sweet	Number (tally)
Curly Chews	
Lemon Sours	
Lollipops	

Puzzle Complete?

Times Tables Summary Test

Two Times Table	Five Times Table	Ten Times Table
1 × 2 = ...	1 × 5 = ...	1 × 10 = ...
2 × 2 = ...	2 × 5 = ...	2 × 10 = ...
3 × 2 = ...	3 × 5 = ...	3 × 10 = ...
4 × 2 = ...	4 × 5 = ...	4 × 10 = ...
5 × 2 = ...	5 × 5 = ...	5 × 10 = ...
6 × 2 = ...	6 × 5 = ...	6 × 10 = ...
7 × 2 = ...	7 × 5 = ...	7 × 10 = ...
8 × 2 = ...	8 × 5 = ...	8 × 10 = ...
9 × 2 = ...	9 × 5 = ...	9 × 10 = ...
10 × 2 = ...	10 × 5 = ...	10 × 10 = ...
11 × 2 = ...	11 × 5 = ...	11 × 10 = ...
12 × 2 = ...	12 × 5 = ...	12 × 10 = ...

Autumn Term

Workout 1 — pages 2-3

1. a) **4** 1 mark   c) **8** 1 mark
   b) **6** 1 mark   d) **10** 1 mark

2. **6 pairs** 1 mark
   12 elephants 1 mark

3. a) **12** 1 mark   d) **18** 1 mark
   b) **24** 1 mark   e) **14** 1 mark
   c) **22** 1 mark   f) **10** 1 mark

Puzzle: Farah the Fish

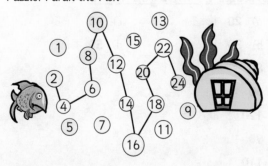

Workout 2 — pages 4-5

1. a) **8** 1 mark   c) **12** 1 mark
   b) **10** 1 mark   d) **14** 1 mark

2. **8 pairs** 1 mark
   16 shoes 1 mark

3. a) **18** 1 mark   d) **6** 1 mark
   b) **16** 1 mark   e) **14** 1 mark
   c) **24** 1 mark   f) **20** 1 mark

Puzzle: Where is Rufus?

$6 \times 2 = $ **12**. 12 = I.
$2 \times 2 = $ **4**. 4 = N.
$1 \times 2 = $ **2**. 2 = T.
$3 \times 2 = $ **6**. 6 = H.
$4 \times 2 = $ **8**. 8 = E.
$8 \times 2 = $ **16**. 16 = P.
$5 \times 2 = $ **10**. 10 = A.
$7 \times 2 = $ **14**. 14 = R
$9 \times 2 = $ **18**. 18 = K

Rufus is **IN THE PARK**

Workout 3 — pages 6-7

1. a) **10** 1 mark   c) **20** 1 mark
   b) **15** 1 mark   d) **25** 1 mark

2. **6 groups** 1 mark
   30 balloons 1 mark

3. a) **50** 1 mark   d) **40** 1 mark
   b) **60** 1 mark   e) **30** 1 mark
   c) **55** 1 mark   f) **45** 1 mark

Puzzle: Molly's Bananas

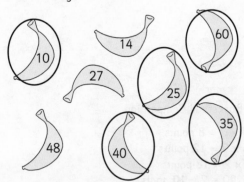

Workout 4 — pages 8-9

1. a) **15** 1 mark   c) **25** 1 mark
   b) **20** 1 mark   d) **30** 1 mark

2. **7 hats** 1 mark
   35 stars 1 mark

3. a) **55** 1 mark   d) **35** 1 mark
   b) **10** 1 mark   e) **40** 1 mark
   c) **50** 1 mark   f) **60** 1 mark

Puzzle: Colour the Rocket

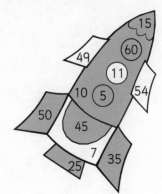

Answers

Workout 5 — pages 10-11

1. a) **4** 1 mark

    b) **2 + 2 + 2 = 6** 1 mark

    c) **2 + 2 + 2 + 2 = 8** 1 mark

    d) **2 + 2 + 2 + 2 + 2 = 10** 1 mark

    e) **2 + 2 + 2 + 2 + 2 + 2 = 12** 1 mark

2. **16** 1 mark

3. **20** 1 mark

4. **24** 1 mark

5. **14** 1 mark

6. **12** 1 mark

7. **8** 1 mark

8. **18** 1 mark

Puzzle: Basketball Competition

Sara: $4 \times 2 = $ **8** points
Lily: $6 \times 2 = $ **12** points
Ash: $9 \times 2 = $ **18** points
Usman: $20 \div 2 = $ **10** goals

Workout 6 — pages 12-13

1. a) **10** 1 mark

    b) **5 + 5 + 5 = 15** 1 mark

    c) **5 + 5 + 5 + 5 = 20** 1 mark

    d) **5 + 5 + 5 + 5 + 5 = 25** 1 mark

    e) **5 + 5 + 5 + 5 + 5 + 5 = 30** 1 mark

2. **55** 1 mark

3. **45** 1 mark

4. **35** 1 mark

5. **50** 1 mark

6. **60** 1 mark

7. **40** 1 mark

8. **15** 1 mark

Puzzle: Kangaroo Jump

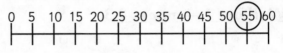

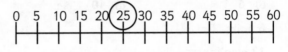

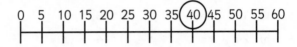

Workout 7 — pages 14-15

1. a) **20** 1 mark   c) **40** 1 mark

    b) **30** 1 mark   d) **50** 1 mark

2. **80** 1 mark

3. **60** 1 mark

4. **120** 1 mark

5. **90** 1 mark

6. **110** 1 mark

7. **70** 1 mark

8. **100** 1 mark

9. **10** 1 mark

Puzzle: Ski Run

Workout 8 — pages 16-17

1. a) **20** 1 mark

   b) **10 + 10 + 10 = 30** 1 mark

   c) **10 + 10 + 10 + 10 + 10 = 50** 1 mark

   d) **10 + 10 + 10 + 10 + 10 +
      10 + 10 = 70** 1 mark

   e) **10 + 10 + 10 + 10 + 10 +
      10 + 10 + 10 = 80** 1 mark

2. **120** 1 mark

3. **70** 1 mark

4. **100** 1 mark

5. **80** 1 mark

6. **90** 1 mark

7. **10** 1 mark

8. **110** 1 mark

Puzzle: Luggage Muddle

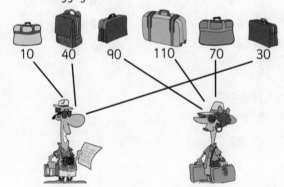

Workout 9 — pages 18-19

1. a) **12** 1 mark   b) **18** 1 mark

2. a) **8** 1 mark   b) **24** 1 mark

3. a) **14** 1 mark   b) **4** 1 mark

4. **10** 1 mark

5. **20** 1 mark

6. **6** 1 mark

7. a) **8 × 2 = 16** so **16 ÷ 2 = 8** 1 mark

   b) **11 × 2 = 22** so **22 ÷ 2 = 11** 1 mark

   c) **4 × 2 = 8** so **8 ÷ 2 = 4** 1 mark

Puzzle: Strawberry Picking

Anwar
**11 × 2
= 22**

Saf
**7 × 2
= 14**

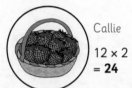

Callie
**12 × 2
= 24**

Ned
**9 × 2
= 18**

Workout 10 — pages 20-21

1. a) **30** 1 mark   b) **80** 1 mark

2. a) **100** 1 mark   b) **50** 1 mark

3. a) **20** 1 mark   b) **110** 1 mark

4. **70** 1 mark

5. **90** 1 mark

6. **10** 1 mark

7. a) **12 × 10 = 12** so 120 ÷ 10 = **12** 1 mark

   b) **4 × 10 = 40** so 40 ÷ 10 = **4** 1 mark

   c) **2 × 10 = 20** so 20 ÷ 10 = **2** 1 mark

Puzzle: Quiz Scores

Team	Score	Star Question?	Cheated?	Total Score
Quiz Masters	2 × 10	✔		**21**
Quiz Heroes	5 × 10		✔	**49**
Quiz Kids	4 × 10	✔	✔	**40**

Workout 11 — pages 22-23

1. a) **35** 1 mark   b) **10** 1 mark

2. a) **55** 1 mark   b) **40** 1 mark

3. a) **20** 1 mark   b) **5** 1 mark

4. **15** 1 mark

5. **30** 1 mark

6. **50** 1 mark

Answers

7. **9** 1 mark

8. **12** 1 mark

9. **5** 1 mark

Puzzle: Digging for Treasure

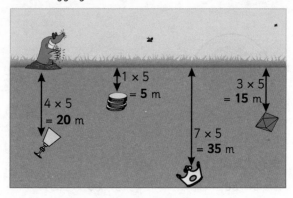

Workout 12 — pages 24-25

1. a) **100** 1 mark   b) **40** 1 mark

2. a) **70** 1 mark   b) **110** 1 mark

3. a) **120** 1 mark   b) **80** 1 mark

4. **50** 1 mark

5. **10** 1 mark

6. **90** 1 mark

7. **3** 1 mark

8. **2** 1 mark

9. **6** 1 mark

Puzzle: Pancake Challenge

Carlo: 100 ÷ 10 = **10 pancakes**
Steffi: 5 × 10 = **50 pancakes**
Ben: 3 × 10 = **30 pancakes**
Dana: 1 × 10 = **10 pancakes**

Steffi's number of pancakes is **more than** Ben's.

Carlo's number of pancakes is **equal to** Dana's.

Dana's number of pancakes is **less than** Steffi's.

Spring Term
Workout 1 — pages 26-27

1. a) **15** 1 mark   b) **25** 1 mark

2. a) **30** 1 mark   b) **4** 1 mark

3. a) **10** 1 mark   b) **40** 1 mark

4. a) **10** 1 mark   c) **55** 1 mark

    b) **35** 1 mark

5. a) **5** 1 mark   c) **60** 1 mark

    b) **45** 1 mark

Puzzle: It's Magic!

    1 × 5 = **5**
    20 − 5 = 15
    3 × 5 = **15**

Workout 2 — pages 28-29

1. a) **18** 1 mark   b) **10** 1 mark

2. a) **6** 1 mark   b) **12** 1 mark

3. a) **4** 1 mark   b) **10** 1 mark

4. **6** pairs 1 mark

    12 gloves 1 mark

5. **2** 1 mark

6. a) **22** 1 mark   c) **8** 1 mark

    b) **14** 1 mark

Puzzle: Circus Seals

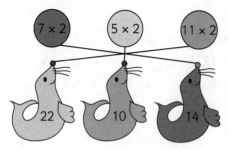

Workout 3 — pages 30-31

1. a) **40** 1 mark   b) **5** 1 mark

2. a) **6** 1 mark   b) **30** 1 mark

3. a) **2** 1 mark   b) **80** 1 mark

4. a) **10** 1 mark   c) **110** 1 mark

   b) **10** 1 mark

5. a) **7** 1 mark   c) **9** 1 mark

   b) **120** 1 mark

Puzzle: Maths Maze

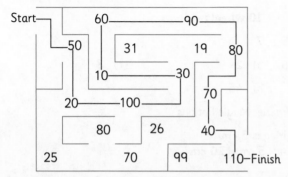

Workout 4 — pages 32-33

1. a) **6** 1 mark   b) **9** 1 mark

2. a) **5** 1 mark   b) **110** 1 mark

3. a) **60** 1 mark   b) **8** 1 mark

4. a) **4** 1 mark   c) **3** 1 mark

   b) **20** 1 mark

5. a) **24** 1 mark   c) **2** 1 mark

   b) **7** 1 mark

Puzzle: Colour the Balloons

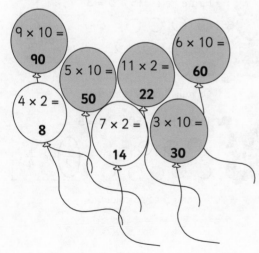

There are **2** yellow balloons.

There are **5** blue balloons.

Workout 5 — pages 34-35

1. a) **35** 1 mark   b) **60** 1 mark

2. a) **20** 1 mark   b) **1** 1 mark

3. a) **8** 1 mark   b) **5** 1 mark

4. a) **12** 1 mark   c) **9** 1 mark

   b) **30** 1 mark

5. a) **20** 1 mark   c) **55** 1 mark

   b) **10** 1 mark

Puzzle: Help Raymond!

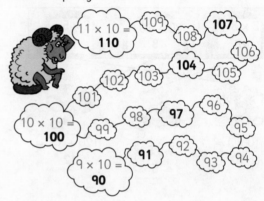

Workout 6 — pages 36-37

1. a) **16** 1 mark   b) **3** 1 mark

2. a) **10** 1 mark   b) **20** 1 mark

3. a) **3** 1 mark   b) **45** 1 mark

4. a) **10** 1 mark   c) **12** 1 mark

   b) **11** 1 mark

5. a) **7** 1 mark   c) **5** 1 mark

   b) **55** 1 mark

Puzzle: Who's the Tallest?

Gertie: 3×2 m = **6 m**

Gordon: 5×1 m = **5 m**

Garry: $8 \div 2$ m = **4 m**

79

Answers

Workout 7 — pages 38-39

1. a) **30** 1 mark   b) **5** 1 mark
2. a) **3** 1 mark   b) **80** 1 mark
3. a) **70** 1 mark   b) **11** 1 mark
4. a) **60** 1 mark   c) **10** 1 mark
   b) **9** 1 mark
5. a) **4** 1 mark   c) **10** 1 mark
   b) **10** 1 mark

Puzzle: Find the Mouse's Hole

Workout 8 — pages 40-41

1. a) **10** 1 mark   b) **3** 1 mark
2. a) **70** 1 mark   b) **22** 1 mark
3. a) **6** 1 mark   b) **5** 1 mark
4. **6** t-shirts 1 mark
   60 spots 1 mark
5. **16** 1 mark
6. a) **120** 1 mark   c) **4** 1 mark
   b) **1** 1 mark

Puzzle: Number Machines

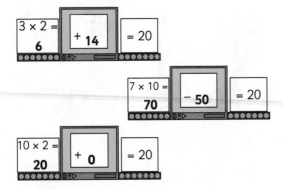

Workout 9 — pages 42-43

1. a) **12** 1 mark   b) **30** 1 mark
2. a) **11** 1 mark   b) **10** 1 mark
3. a) **9** 1 mark   b) **8** 1 mark
4. **5 bikes** 1 mark
   10 wheels 1 mark
5. **7** 1 mark
6. a) **24** 1 mark   c) **3** 1 mark
   b) **45** 1 mark

Puzzle: Magic Potions

Meg is **5 cm** tall
4 × 5 cm = **20 cm**

Workout 10 — pages 44-45

1. a) **14** 1 mark   b) **10** 1 mark
2. a) **11** 1 mark   b) **6** 1 mark
3. a) **60** 1 mark   b) **3** 1 mark
4. a) **16** 1 mark   b) **2** 1 mark
5. a) **9** 1 mark   b) **120** 1 mark
6. **2** 1 mark
7. 4 × 10 = **40 spots** 1 mark

Puzzle: Pirate Treasure!

 Pirate Pete: 15 ÷ 5 = **3**

 $\frac{1}{2}$ or $\boxed{\frac{1}{4}}$

Or any 3 coins coloured.

 Pirate Paul: 50 ÷ 10 = **5**

$\boxed{\frac{1}{2}}$ or $\frac{1}{4}$

Or any 5 coins coloured.

Workout 11 — pages 46-47

1. a) **20** 1 mark   b) **12** 1 mark
2. a) **7** 1 mark   b) **20** 1 mark
3. a) **9** 1 mark   b) **8** 1 mark
4. a) **6** 1 mark   b) **12** 1 mark
5. a) **4** 1 mark   b) **55** 1 mark
6. **8** 1 mark
7. 2 × 5 = **10 treats** 1 mark

Puzzle: Which Broomstick?

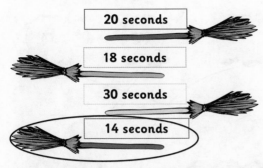

Workout 12 — pages 48-49

1. a) **20** 1 mark   b) **9** 1 mark
2. a) **8** 1 mark   b) **70** 1 mark
3. a) **11** 1 mark   b) **2** 1 mark
4. a) **30** 1 mark   b) **6** 1 mark
5. a) **50** 1 mark   b) **3** 1 mark
6. **60** 1 mark
7. 9 × 10 = **90 sweets** 1 mark

Puzzle: Balance the Scales

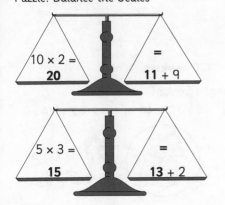

Summer Term
Workout 1 — pages 50-51

1. a) **14** 1 mark   b) **10** 1 mark
2. a) **4** 1 mark   b) **11** 1 mark
3. a) **2** 1 mark   b) **8** 1 mark
4. a) **6** 1 mark   b) **7** 1 mark
5. a) **60** 1 mark   b) **10** 1 mark
6. **120** 1 mark
7. 4 × 2 = **8 wheels** 1 mark

Puzzle: Moon Maths

Uggle   Beeza   Oog   Rog

Workout 2 — pages 52-53

1. a) **20** 1 mark   b) **7** 1 mark
2. a) **7** 1 mark   b) **60** 1 mark
3. a) **5** 1 mark   b) **9** 1 mark
4. a) **10** 1 mark   b) **25** 1 mark
5. a) **11** 1 mark   b) **40** 1 mark
6. **10** 1 mark
7. 3 × 5 = **15 slices** 1 mark

Puzzle: Jumping Around

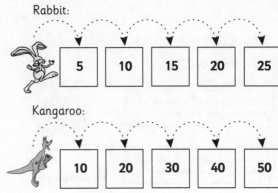

Answers

Workout 3 — pages 54-55

1. a) **18** 1 mark   b) **8** 1 mark
2. a) **40** 1 mark   b) **11** 1 mark
3. a) **14** 1 mark   b) **11** 1 mark
4. a) **6** 1 mark   b) **50** 1 mark
5. a) **7** 1 mark   b) **10** 1 mark
6. **5** 1 mark
7. $6 \times 5 =$ **30 ducklings** 1 mark

Puzzle: Crossing the River

Workout 4 — pages 56-57

1. a) **18** 1 mark   b) **35** 1 mark
2. a) **15** 1 mark   b) **4** 1 mark
3. a) **60** 1 mark   b) **22** 1 mark
4. a) **12** 1 mark   c) **80** 1 mark
   b) **11** 1 mark
5. a) **8** 1 mark   c) **3** 1 mark
   b) **45** 1 mark

Puzzle: Match the Shapes!

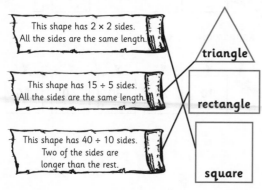

Workout 5 — pages 58-59

1. a) **2** 1 mark   b) **20** 1 mark
2. a) **2** 1 mark   b) **1** 1 mark
3. a) **50** 1 mark   b) **4** 1 mark
4. a) **12** 1 mark   c) **70** 1 mark
   b) **25** 1 mark
5. a) **2** 1 mark   c) **9** 1 mark
   b) **6** 1 mark

Puzzle: Piggy Banks

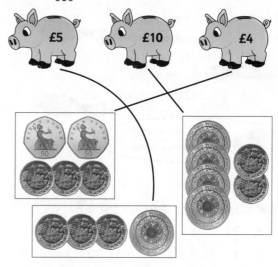

Workout 6 — pages 60-61

1. a) **10** 1 mark   b) **2** 1 mark
2. a) **1** 1 mark   b) **100** 1 mark
3. a) **2** 1 mark   b) **14** 1 mark
4. a) **20** 1 mark   b) **8** 1 mark
5. a) **110** 1 mark   b) **12** 1 mark
6. **50** 1 mark
7. $12 \times 10 =$ **120 cookies** 1 mark

Puzzle: The Longest Snake Contest

$6 \times 5 =$ **30 m** $4 \times 10 =$ **40 m** $12 \times 2 =$ **24 m**

$40 - 24 =$ **16 m longer**

Workout 7 — pages 62-63

1. a) **9** 1 mark   b) **40** 1 mark

2. a) **55** 1 mark   b) **3** 1 mark

3. a) **6** 1 mark   b) **22** 1 mark

4. a) **6** 1 mark   b) **7** 1 mark

5. a) **8** 1 mark   b) **16** 1 mark

6. **30** 1 mark

7. 12 × 5 = **60 seeds** 1 mark

Puzzle: The Corner Shop

     30 ÷ 5 = **6 lemon fizzers**

     90 – 30 = **60p left**

     20 ÷ 2 = **2 jelly frogs**

     60 – 20 = **40p left**

Workout 8 — pages 64-65

1. a) **1** 1 mark   b) **50** 1 mark

2. a) **9** 1 mark   b) **2** 1 mark

3. a) **10** 1 mark   b) **1** 1 mark

4. a) **3** 1 mark   b) **8** 1 mark

5. a) **4** 1 mark   b) **7** 1 mark

6. 9 × 10 = **90 points** 1 mark

7. 25 ÷ 5 = **5 red laces** 1 mark

Puzzle: Space Time

     9 × 5 minutes = 45 minutes

     He finished flying at **quarter to three**.

Workout 9 — pages 66-67

1. a) **5** 1 mark   b) **2** 1 mark

2. a) **30** 1 mark   b) **7** 1 mark

3. a) **1** 1 mark   b) **10** 1 mark

4. a) **10** 1 mark   b) **24** 1 mark

5. a) **11** 1 mark   b) **2** 1 mark

6. 12 × 10 = **120 flowers** 1 mark

7. 8 × 5 = **40 cherries** 1 mark

Puzzle: Suitcase Mix-up!

> Suzie's first suitcase has:
>
> 80 ÷ 10 in the tens place = **8**
>
> 4 ÷ 2 in the ones place = **2**
>
> Suzie's second suitcase has:
>
> 1 × 5 in the tens place = **5**
>
> 3 × 2 in the ones place = **6**

Workout 10 — pages 68-69

1. a) **12** 1 mark   b) **10** 1 mark

2. a) **5** 1 mark   b) **2** 1 mark

3. a) **10** 1 mark   b) **30** 1 mark

4. a) **4** 1 mark   b) **5** 1 mark

5. a) **45** 1 mark   b) **60** 1 mark

6. 5 × 2 = **10 pieces** 1 mark

7. 11 × 5 = **55 carrots** 1 mark

Answers

Puzzle: How Many Animals?

$3 \times 5 = 15$

$7 \times 2 = 14$

$15 + 14 = \textbf{29 animals}$

Workout 11 — pages 70-71

1. a) **2** 1 mark   b) **40** 1 mark
2. a) **3** 1 mark   b) **7** 1 mark
3. a) **50** 1 mark   b) **5** 1 mark
4. a) **9** 1 mark   b) **11** 1 mark
5. a) **12** 1 mark   b) **12** 1 mark
6. $3 \times 10 = \textbf{30 bees}$ 1 mark
7. $6 \times 10 = \textbf{60 pins}$ 1 mark

Puzzle: Colour the Shapes
Answers may vary — any answer with the correct number of sections for each shape shaded is valid.

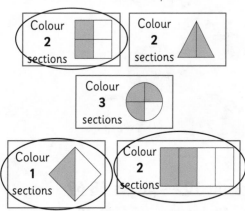

Colour **2** sections

Colour **2** sections

Colour **3** sections

Colour **1** sections

Colour **2** sections

Workout 12 — pages 72-73

1. a) **8** 1 mark   b) **2** 1 mark
2. a) **25** 1 mark   b) **2** 1 mark
3. a) **30** 1 mark   b) **10** 1 mark
4. a) **10** 1 mark   b) **35** 1 mark
5. a) **8** 1 mark   b) **22** 1 mark

6. $40 \div 5 = \textbf{8 flies}$ 1 mark
7. $9 \times 10 = \textbf{90 pens}$ 1 mark

Puzzle: At the Sweet Shop

Sweet	Number (tally)
Curly Chews	ЖЖ ЖЖ ЖЖ I
Lemon Sours	ЖЖ ЖЖ ЖЖ
Lollipops	ЖЖ ЖЖ ЖЖ ЖЖ

M2TXW11